Understanding Emotions

Photocopiable activities to help
children to recognise and explore emotions

Mark & Katy Hill

Permission to photocopy

The rights of Mark and Katy Hill to be identified as the authors of this work have been asserted by them in accordance with sections 77 and 78 of the Copyright, Designs and Patents Act 1988.

Understanding Emotions
102171
ISBN-13: 978 1 85503 475 4

Printed in the UK for LDA
Victoria Business Park, Pintail Close, Netherfield, Nottingham, NG4 2SG

Contents

Teacher's notes

The *Understanding Emotions* materials have been designed to aid children in their exploration and recognition of facial expressions, emotions and related vocabulary within situational and sensory contexts.

The emotions discussed are divided into two groups to develop a language of emotion that is intended to be meaningful to children:

• Group 1: happy, sad, angry, scared, excited, surprised
• Group 2: worried, lonely, proud, ashamed, disappointed, jealous

The intention of these materials is that a child will work through the basic emotions listed in Group 1 before moving on to Group 2. The selected emotions perhaps best represent the feelings that may be experienced in situations in which children might commonly find themselves. The premise from which we start is that an emotion is a response to, at least in part, some external sensory stimuli, whether within a single sensory channel or a combination of sensory channels. For example, fear resulting from a loud sound, happiness resulting from having and giving a cuddle, jealousy resulting from not being given the largest slice of cake. By encouraging a child to identify some of the possible sensory experiences associated with an emotion they may become more able to construct meaning around their feelings and those of others. While exploring the materials the child should think about each emotion in a range of sensory contexts – What is happy in the auditory, visual, olfactory (smell), gustatory (taste) and tactile channel? For example, if a child has an ice cream, is it the sound of licking the ice cream or the taste that engages the emotion?

The book has been divided into sections that explore emotions in a variety of contexts involving individuals and groups of people, changing emotions, predicting emotions, understanding emotion within its cause and effect, and sequencing emotions.

Some of the constituent parts of emotional understanding have been separated: facial expression, thought, speech and environmental context. It is essential when completing the activities to support them with practical examples and role-play. In this way, a child can look for other aspects of emotional expression such as posture, body language, voice intonation and voice volume. It is also important that an emotional vocabulary be taught so that a child can talk about their emotions and those of others. The activities aim to explore the many different ways of 'knowing' an emotion in order to assimilate an emotional vocabulary label for that unknown feeling that they may experience when they enjoy playing on a favourite piece of park equipment, listening to a particular piece of music, or eating a favourite food. Draw the child's attention to the possibility that emotions can be grouped and catagorised and encourage them to associate vocabulary within each emotional concept.

All the activities must be approached slowly and methodically due to the complexity of emotions and their comprehension. A child will work through a range of skills moving from acquisition of a skill *receptively* (i.e. identifying an expression/emotion or identifying a context for emotion on request) before working *expressively* to talk about emotions in a given context or to talk reflectively about emotions. They will have opportunities to talk about the emotion in others (externally) and within themselves (internally). Initially limit or isolate information leading to an identified emotion. Present information slowly allowing the child time to process an element thoroughly before showing them in combinations as this will avoid overloading the child with too many concurrent features to process (e.g. facial expression, gesture, context, voice pitch/volume).

An essential skill in recognising emotion is to gain a situational understanding of that emotion. A child needs to be able to recognise a facial expression, know which emotion it represents and which emotion applies to a given situation. For example, if a boy has fallen off his bike, in this situation, the boy is feeling sad. The child also needs to understand that other people may not think the same as themselves – Can they put themselves in someone else's shoes to talk about what that person might be seeing, hearing, saying, thinking, feeling or believing? The teaching of emotion within a group can be particularly useful, especially if the group includes children who are able to talk in more detail about how they feel. These children bring their own knowledge and understanding to support a child who is less emotionally literate. Through group-based work a child will experience different perspectives and become aware of the reasons for them, thereby creating an opportunity to understand that others can think and feel differently. Adults should talk about their own emotions, the emotions of the target child (if appropriate) and the child's peers as and when opportunities arise.

Importantly, you should not rely solely on these materials in teaching an emotion. They should be supported by the identification of facial expression and emotion in real-life situations.

Essential note

The emotions of a person, be it an adult or a child, are fragile and their protection should be paramount in any activity. At no point should a child be forced to share their feelings or made to feel that not sharing them is unacceptable. Any child experiencing emotional disturbance should be referred to the relevant support services. Likewise, it is conceivable that during a discussion about emotions a child may make a disclosure. In such an instance this information must be passed on to designated senior staff.

Some children who have sensory-based difficulties, particularly those that manifest as hypersensitivity, may find discussion triggers the recall of painful experiences. This should be handled with sensitivity and it would be prudent to seek information and agreement from parents/carers before working with a child.

Instructions

Recognising and naming emotions

Activity 1 Matching assessment activity (pages 9 and 10)

This activity may be used as an initial assessment of a child's understanding and use of emotional vocabulary. Cover the emotion labels on page 9, is the child able to point at the correct facial expression when it is named (receptive) and name the emotion when shown specific expressions (expressive)? Photocopy both pages. Initially, use page 9 to discuss the individual facial features and how they differ for each emotion. Now cut out the images from both pages to make cards. Then encourage the child to name and match the cards that have an added distracting visual feature on page 10 (e.g. earrings, moustaches, long/short hair) to the facial expressions from page 9.

These sheets can be used for developing a memory task by copying page 10 twice and playing pelmanism, or by using the cards to play a version of Kim's game where the child has to identify which emotion card has been removed. Discuss the methods the child used to recall the missing expression.

The facial expressions on page 9 can be used to support all of the activities as they provide a useful reminder of which facial features show each of the emotions discussed.

Activity 2 Emotions expression template (pages 11 and 12)

This activity will draw the child's attention to the importance of each facial feature when looking for clues about how someone might be feeling.

Photocopy both pages. Page 11 has a blank face outline. Page 12 contains facial features to be cut out and then placed in position on the blank face. A different version of a facial feature can be placed on the blank face to change the emotion depicted. The expressions to be explored are shown at the bottom of the page.

Initially, simply compare each facial feature for similarities and differences, then progress to creating whole expressions. In the first instance limit the features available to two emotions so that the choice is smaller, then increase the choice and difficulty by asking the child to choose the correct features for a particular emotion from a larger selection. Revisit this activity regularly so that the child can work gradually towards the construction of each expression from memory.

Discussing emotions from a sensory perspective

Activity 3 Exploring emotions through the senses (pages 13, 14 and 15)

In this activity the child explores how an emotion is sparked in them. How do the activities, people and objects in their lives make them feel? What role do their senses have in the way their emotions manifest themselves?

Two completed examples are given – Happy and Angry. Begin by asking the child to discuss what makes them happy in relation to their senses. For example, the child may feel happy when eating an ice cream, seeing family and friends, hearing a funny joke. Symbols have been used to denote the senses (e.g. ear for hearing, eye for sight).

Now explore the second example looking at anger. The child can then build their own map of an emotion using a photocopy of the blank template provided. Working as part of a group will help the child to gain an understanding of an emotion by drawing together the thoughts and ideas offered by others.

Activity 4 Sensory search task (pages 16 and 17)

The child circles an emotion (e.g. scared) and identifies things that might make them feel that emotion in a sensory channel by drawing a line from the sensory symbol to an item in the picture. For example, the child might decide that the noise of the school bell ringing is scary, so they would draw a line from the ear (auditory sensory channel) to the school bell in the picture. Initially a child may feel more comfortable discussing the emotions and reactions of a character in the scene rather than their own responses.

The child should think and talk about their own and others emotions relating to the broad scene depicted.

Discussing contexts

Activity 5 Context discussion task (pages 18 and 19)

Some children find it difficult to look for the emotional clues in different contexts. This activity is intended to help equip a child with the skills to read a situation successfully. Look together at the first scene. What objects can they see? What might that tell them about where the scene is set? Now look at the people within the scene. Can the child work out the relationships between the characters? The child should discuss the general context of the picture and talk about their own experiences with respect to that situation. Encourage them to identify the important elements of the picture and how they are related (e.g. the man is sliding on the ice – the ice is frozen – it is winter – he is wearing warm clothes – falling over hurts). Once all the clues have been discussed the child can begin to explore facial expression, particularly where the characters are demonstrating different emotions while taking part in the same activity (e.g. sledging down the hill).

Activity 6 Context (pages 20 and 21)

A crucial part of understanding and recognising facial expression and emotion is interpreting the context in which it is encountered. Discuss the content of each picture with the child and what it means to them. For each picture they should try to identify the emotion that may be experienced and offer reasons for their answer. Make sure that where appropriate you discuss the sensory experiences that might be involved in the images shown. For example, the exploding cracker might make them feel excited because they can see the prizes inside, or the loud bang as the cracker is pulled apart may make them feel scared.

Activity 7 Draw the event (page 22)

The child is presented with two sources of information – visual and auditory. Photocopy the page and cut out the visual clue strip for each of the contexts without the scene title. The adult reads out the verbal clues encouraging the child to identify the context being described. The visual clues are designed to provide a simplified level of information on which to make a judgement. They are arranged so that those that are more obvious in description of the context are at the end of the set. In this way, the entire set of pictures could be covered and presented one at a time. This allows the adult to show the visual and auditory clues in a range of combinations and therefore differentiate the task to suit an individual child. The child should draw the context which they feel is correct given the clues they have seen and heard. They then discuss the emotions that could be generated within those contexts and the reasons for them.

Discussing emotions of a character

Activity 8 How do they feel? (page 23)

The child should try to identify the emotion involved in the event depicted. In this first activity, focusing on the Group 1 emotions, the emotion is unambiguous. The child could cut and paste (using the faces on page 48) or draw the expression onto the blank face in each scene. Ask the child to talk about the context of the image to ensure that they have identified the relevant details. If they are struggling to identify the emotion associated with the scenario they may benefit from being presented with a 'forced alternative' (i.e. give two verbal choices) initially, ensuring that the correct answer is obvious. Encourage them to talk about the choice they make.

Activity 9 What's the emotion? (pages 24 and 25)

Activities 9 and 10 encourage the child to understand and talk about facial expressions and emotions in a range of familiar contexts. In these activities the character scenarios have been drawn to be ambiguous in their interpretation. The child should discuss the possible emotions and expressions of the characters depicted in relation to themselves and their peers. Crucially, this highlights the existence of multiple perspectives to the scenarios.

This activity comprises of a set of twelve pictures depicting an individual in a given context without a facial expression. The child should choose an expression they feel best represents the correct emotion to go with each picture. Those children who are able to faithfully represent the expression may draw it on the blank face; alternatively they could cut and paste the emotion from the template page (page 48).

Discussing emotions of additional characters

Activity 10 What are their emotions? – Additional character (pages 26 and 27)

The child must decide how the two characters in each scene are feeling and fill in their blank faces. The intention of this task is to demonstrate that people can feel differently within the same scenario. It may be beneficial to introduce this task by presenting the child or group of children with an object and simply identifying who likes it / who does not like it and why. The child must try to offer an explanation for the emotions they have chosen for each of the characters.

Activity 11 What are their emotions? – Additional characters (page 28)

When we are in a group we can have different emotional responses to the same situation. This often depends on our point of view and role in the action. Ask the child to decide how each of the characters in the scenes shown is feeling. Why do they think that they might feel this way? The child should draw each of their chosen emotions onto the relevant character's blank face. If necessary they could use the facial expressions on page 9 as a prompt to make sure that they have remembered all the facial features needed to depict the emotion. Again, relate the choice of emotions back to possible sensory causes. Is this a possible explanation for different perspectives?

Discussing emotions and expressions with additional speech and thought

Activity 12 What's the emotion? – The language of emotion (pages 29 and 30)

Page 29 explores Group 1 emotions, page 30, Group 2 emotions. The child draws a line to match each facial expression with its label. They then link the facial expression and label with the speech they feel represents that emotion. It is important that the adult reads out the speech so they can add or remove intonation, gesture and body language as required. In this way the child could revisit the same task a number of times, each time being provided with more clues. The use of additional clues allows for differentiation. Through watching the adult model the physical actions and behaviours that accompany an emotion the child can learn about body language and gesture.

Activity 13 Thinking about how we feel (pages 31 and 32)

The child uses a pencil line to match each facial expression with its label. They then link the label and related expression to an appropriate thought representing that emotion.

The child may work with an adult or a group where more able readers could support if necessary. It is important that through discussion the child continues to learn that facial expressions, emotions and thoughts might not be in agreement; e.g. a child might be smiling as a friend takes a cake, but is really thinking, 'I want that cake. Why should you have it when you've already had two?' (angry).

Activity 14 Emotion match (pages 33 and 34)

The child must fill in the blank faces with an emotion that they feel is suitable for each character. They may discover that what the character is thinking and saying make it difficult to decide which expression to choose. Will the child choose to show the emotion that matches the speech or the thought?

If you are working with a group of children ask them to agree on a context (or provide one if necessary) and consider the thoughts and speech in light of this. Again, discuss that thought, facial expression and speech may not be in agreement. Can the child(ren) think of examples where these aspects do not agree?

Discussing emotions from verbal scenarios

Activity 15 Verbal scenarios (pages 35 and 36)

Ideally this activity would be completed with a group of children; however, a version without the voting cards could be played when working one-to-one with a child. The group is presented with a scenario from those listed on page 35. This can either be read out by the adult or the children can each be given a photocopy of the page. The children must decide together, giving reasons, on the emotion associated with the given scenario.

It is important to include children who are more emotionally literate to support others who are having difficulty accessing the task, and for the adult to lead the discussion. On occasions when a child is struggling to make sense of a scenario, a forced alternative could be given by presenting the child with two verbal examples, one that is obviously correct and one that is obviously incorrect. Over time the child would be offered choices that were more subtle in their differences. The cards on page 36 can be photocopied, so that each child has a set, and used by the children to secretly show what they think the emotion is. The group can then come to a consensus without the children relying on their peers for clues.

Discussing changes of emotions

Activity 16 Comparing levels of emotions (pages 37 and 38)

Photocopy the pages and cut out each set of images in turn. Present the child with a set of pictures depicting three scenarios for a Group 1 emotion. Begin by talking through the scenarios to establish understanding. Ask the child to place the scenes in an order that for them represents an increasing strength of that emotion, (e.g. happy, happier, happiest or angry, angrier, angriest). In each instance the child should try to give reasons for their chosen order and then go on to make a comparison with a peer's or the adult's choice.

This activity will establish an understanding of comparative language in relation to emotional vocabulary and help the child to realise that any emotion may be experienced at a variety of intensities.

Activity 17 Basic changing emotions activity (page 39)

This activity supports the child in recognising that emotions can change. As an introduction to this concept the task focuses on a change from just one emotion to its antithesis (unhappy to happy) and remains with this through a number of scenarios to consolidate this idea. The child is presented with a single scenario which depicts 'unhappy' and must draw a scene next to it that would make the scenario a 'happy' one.

This activity demonstrates to the child that sometimes emotions change over a long period of time but they can also change almost instantly. Which of these result from a change in sensory experience?

Activity 18 Changing emotions (pages 40 and 41)

Photocopy the pages. Ask the child to cut out the pictures from the bottom of the page and place them between the pairs of faces. The chosen picture should change the emotion on the left to that on the right, e.g. you were feeling worried, then the bee went out of the window and you are now feeling happy.

This activity develops the child's awareness that their own and others' emotions are not static. In discussion, the child should identify possible causes for changes of emotion, e.g. what someone says, how they act, a look they give you and so on.

They could also reflect on which emotions tend to be felt consecutively, if any, and whether you can feel two emotions at the same time, e.g. Why do people cry if they are happy?

Discussing sequences of emotions

Activity 19 Cause and effect (pages 42 and 43)

Begin by asking the child to discuss the scene depicted. They then draw a possible outcome in the square next to each scene. For this activity it is important that the child understands and can use temporal vocabulary appropriately, e.g. first, next, last, before, after and so on. Initially it would be prudent to assess the child's ability to predict. Additionally, it is important to discuss the notion that what you feel now might be based on what happened previously, what is happening currently or what might happen in the future. Encourage the child to think about how the character might feel. They then draw the emotion they think best matches the emotional effect of the outcome they have drawn. For example, if the child reaches for a boat on the water, falls in and gets soaked, they may feel sad, but if they reach the boat successfully, they might feel happy or proud.

Activity 20 What happens next? (pages 44 and 45)

Ask the child to discuss the scenario presented on the left. Encourage them to talk about what the outcome might be, based on different emotions. For example, if the scene shows a child choosing the biggest cake – what would happen next if the child felt happy, angry, sad or surprised? Make sure that they think about how the senses relate to this, for example, Why might they be sad with a cake in front of them? Because they don't like the taste. The child should fill in the blank face with their chosen emotion and then draw the outcome based on that selected emotion in the box on the right, e.g. fill the blank face in the cake scene with an angry expression and then draw an adult taking the cake from the child. The outcome picture is therefore determind and limited by the emotion chosen.

Activities 21 and 22 Emotions changing in sequence (pages 46 and 47)

Activity 21 contains two 3-step sequences where the child should draw the facial expressions onto the characters. Encourage them to talk through the narrative and how the emotions relate to the events. How and why are the emotions changing? Remind them to look for emotional clues from the body language shown, the context and all sensory channels.

Activity 22 contains two 4-step sequences to be discussed and completed in the same way. The additional scene allows for more detailed discussion about how quickly emotions can change and what might prompt this change.

Facial expressions template page (page 48)

This page can be photocopied and the facial expressions cut and pasted into position for all activities involving the filling in of blank faces.

Further activities

There are many enjoyable and practical ways in which children may consolidate the skills learnt through carrying out the tasks in this book. Here are a few suggestions:

- Memory expressions: use the facial expression cards (p. 9 or p. 10). Place them face up on the table so that the child can see them. Using a duplicate card for one of the emotions on the table, briefly show the child the card before removing it. The child must then find the matching expression on the table from memory.
- The child could use a mirror to explore their own facial expressions before drawing them.
- Collect a series of digital photos of the class to make a montage of expressions.
- Play 'Guess the emotion' from a single facial element (e.g. eye brow position). You could use the features on p.12 for this or cover parts of faces in magazine pictures.
- Make clay / papier-mâché / Plasticene® faces depicting emotions which the child must try to identify from touch alone. They could then make their own emotion faces.
- Listen to different pieces of music and discuss the emotions that are evoked.
- Use mime. The children could take turns to mime an event and the associated emotion, e.g. eating an ice cream and dropping it on the floor.
- Emotion circle game: the group sit in a circle and a child is chosen to be 'on' and leaves the room briefly so they are unaware of who is chosen to be the leader of the group. The leader decides on an emotion to show through facial expression and the group copies. The leader may change the emotion at any point and the group must follow. The child chosen to be 'on' returns and must work out who is leading the group.
- Play 'Slow-motion emotion' during which children take turns to change their facial expression slowly. Peers must guess which emotion is being presented.
- Find your friend: pairs of children are provided with a card naming an emotion and/or depicting the associated facial expression. They must make this expression and then find their partner making the same emotional expression.
- Children take turns to read a very short story in a happy, sad, angry, scared or surprised manner.
- Use a 'feely bag' and place a single object in it without the object being seen. The children pass it around the group, saying one thing about the object. They should not name the object but instead look at their peers' faces to see if their expressions offer clues to how they feel about what is in the bag. Also, the children should be encouraged to notice that they are saying different things about the same object denoting different perspectives.

Facial expressions

Happy   Sad   Angry

Scared   Excited   Surprised

Worried   Lonely   Proud

Ashamed   Disappointed   Jealous

Can you discover how each character is feeling?

Change my expression to match the emotions shown at the bottom of the page.

Happy   **Sad**   **Angry**   **Scared**   **Excited**   **Surprised**

Facial features

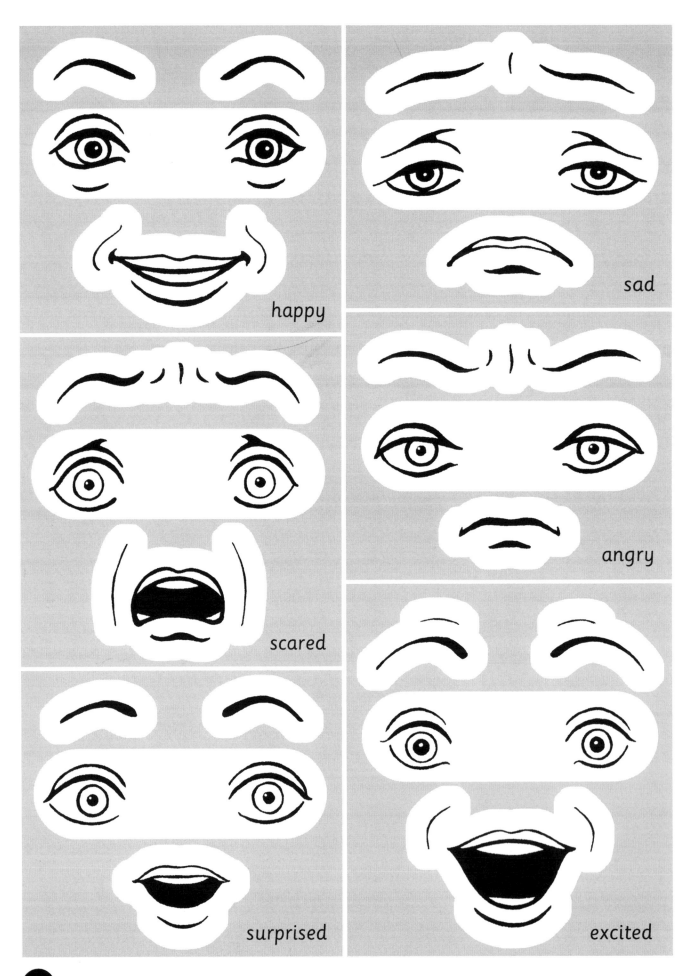

happy

sad

scared

angry

surprised

excited

What makes me feel ...

Happy

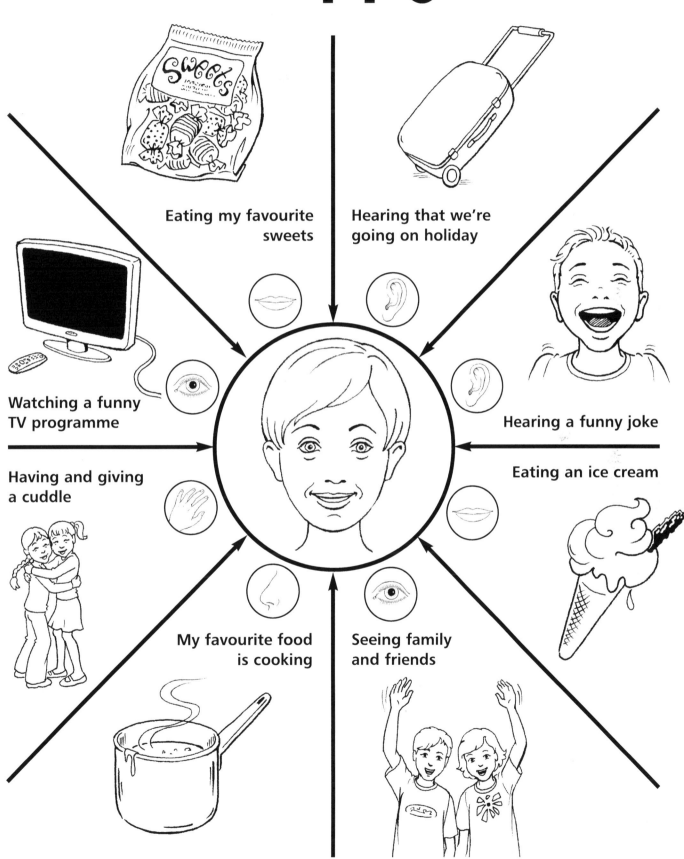

Eating my favourite sweets

Hearing that we're going on holiday

Watching a funny TV programme

Hearing a funny joke

Having and giving a cuddle

Eating an ice cream

My favourite food is cooking

Seeing family and friends

What makes me feel ...

Angry

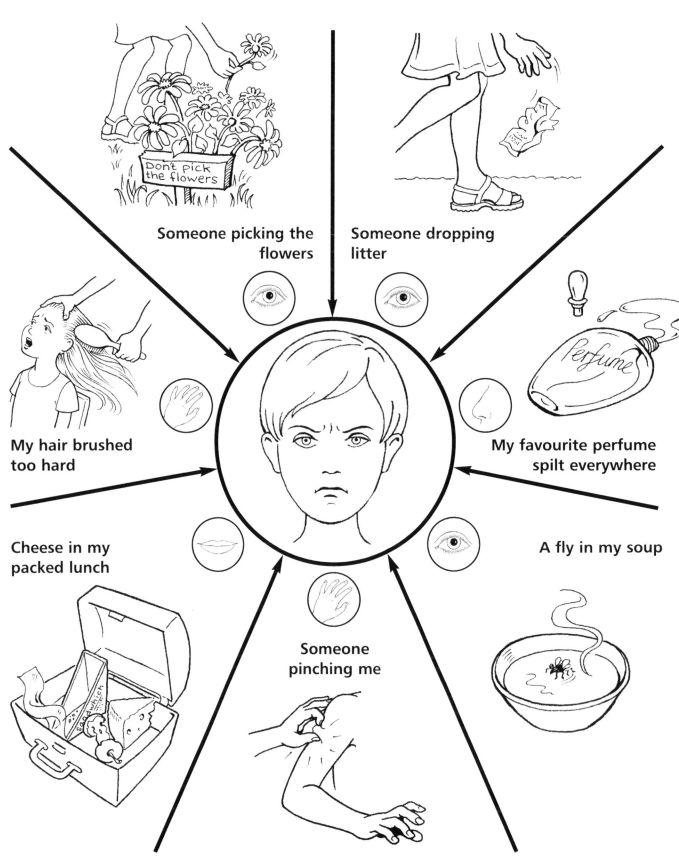

Someone picking the flowers

Someone dropping litter

My hair brushed too hard

My favourite perfume spilt everywhere

Cheese in my packed lunch

A fly in my soup

Someone pinching me

Permission to Photocopy

What makes me feel ...

_____

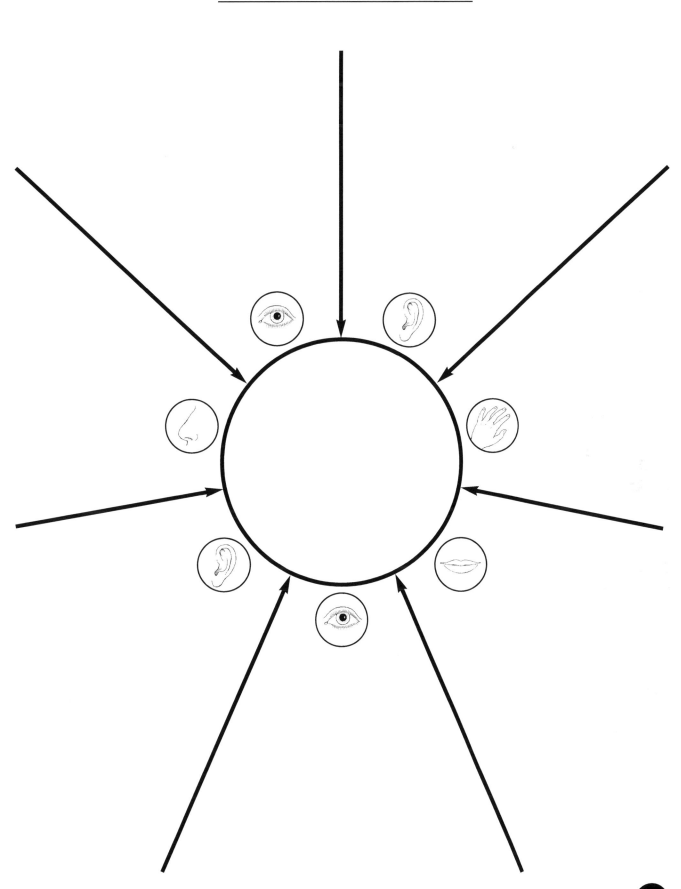

Choose an emotion and look for things in the picture that might make the character feel that way. Match the items you find to the sense used.

Happy   **Sad**   **Angry**   **Scared**   **Excited**   **Surprised**

Worried   **Lonely**   **Proud**   **Ashamed**   **Disappointed**   **Jealous**

Choose an emotion and look for things in the picture that might make the character feel that way. Match the items you find to the sense used.

Happy   **Sad**   **Angry**   **Scared**   **Excited**   **Surprised**

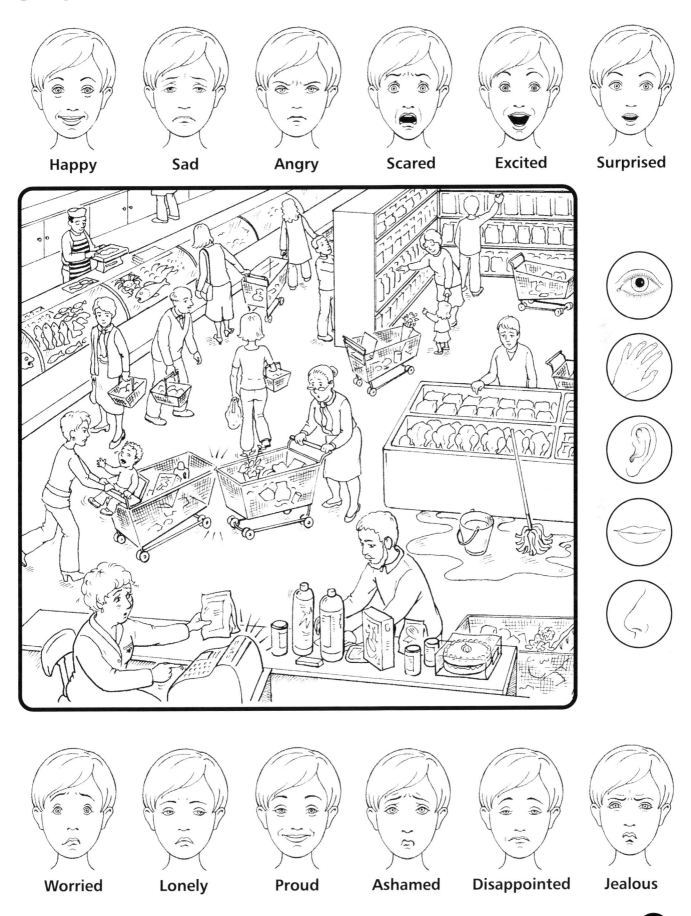

Worried   **Lonely**   **Proud**   **Ashamed**   **Disappointed**   **Jealous**

Can you find the clues in the scene below that show what is happening and how the characters feel?

Can you find the clues in the scene below that show what is happening and how the characters feel?

Which emotion(s) might you feel in these situations?

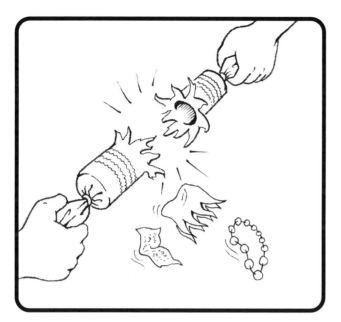

Which emotion(s) might you feel in these situations?

21

Where is it? Listen and look at the clues to help you draw the scene.

1. School scene

2. Farmyard scene

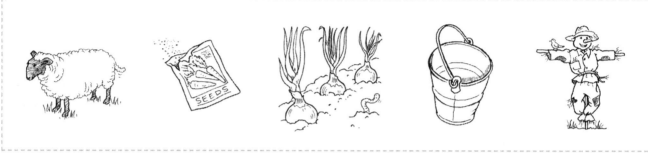

3. Shopping scene

4. Birthday scene

1. School scene – Adult reads: a computer, a whiteboard, paint and brushes, children sitting, a teacher talking, drawers opening

2. Farmyard scene – Adult reads: cows mooing, tractor, dog barking, fields

3. Shopping scene – Adult reads: doors opening and closing, people talking, cars, buildings

4. Birthday scene – Adult reads: children eating, sandwiches, crisps, music, invitation, balloons

How do they feel?

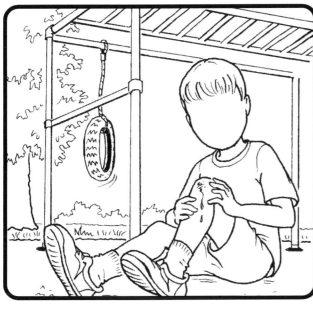

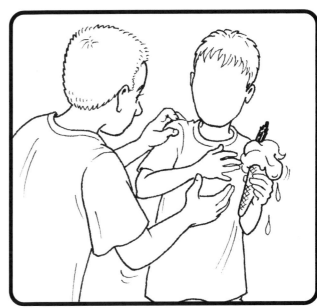

Can you work out how each of the characters is feeling?

Can you work out how each of the characters is feeling?

How do the characters feel in each of these situations?

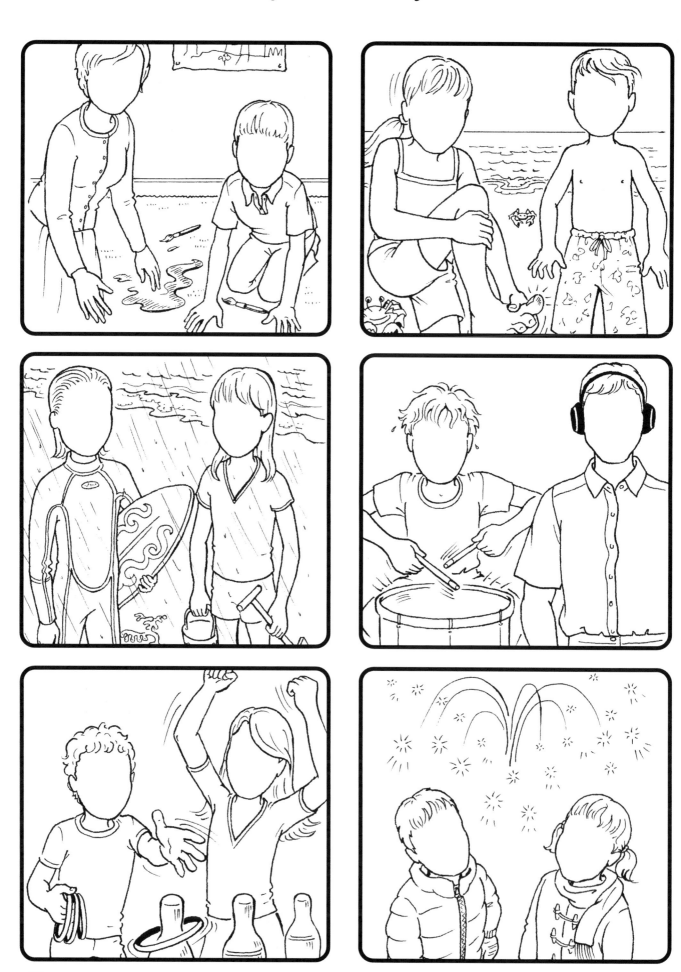

How do the characters feel in each of these situations?

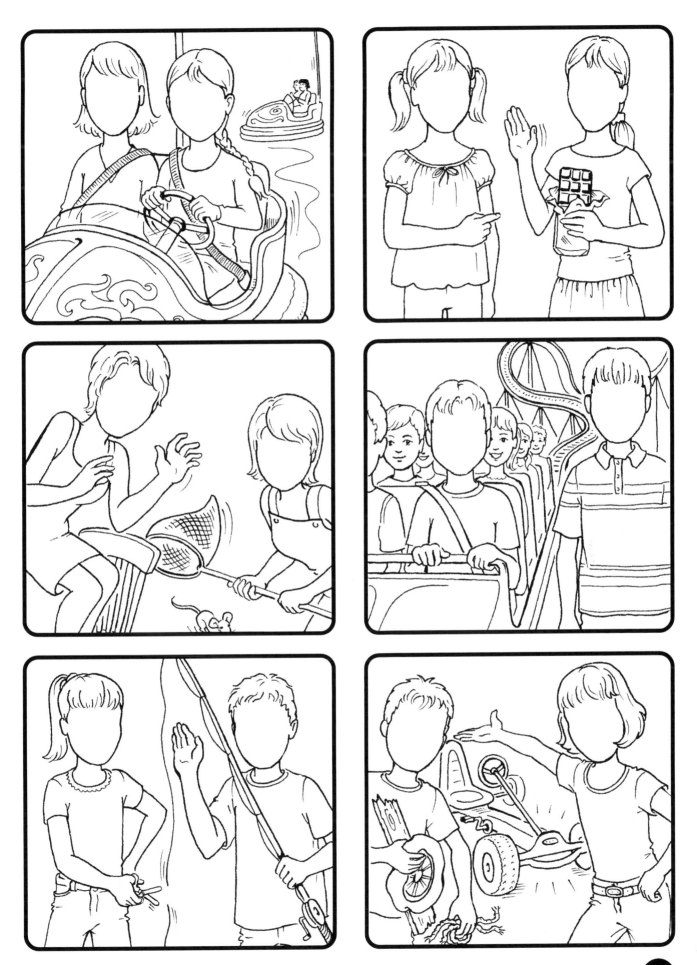

How does each character feel in the scenes below?
Do they all feel the same way?

Permission to Photocopy

Can you match the facial expression with its label and find the speech you think best fits that emotion?

angry

scared

excited

sad

happy

surprised

My dog has hurt his paw.

The teacher really liked my writing.

I can't wait to go on holiday.

You have lost the ball again.

I didn't know that you were coming round this afternoon.

It looks a long way down from up here.

Permission to Photocopy

Can you match the facial expression with its label and find the speech you think best fits that emotion?

proud

ashamed

jealous

disappointed

worried

lonely

I'm sorry that I took your snack without asking.

I wish I had someone to go swimming with.

Your coat is so much nicer than mine.

I'm really glad that I won the music prize this year.

I'm not sure that I am going to pass the maths test today.

I thought that my race time would be faster than that.

Can you match the facial expression with its label and find the thought you think best fits that emotion?

excited

That loud noise made me jump.

scared

That's the last time I let him borrow anything.

angry

I can't wait to go to her party.

happy

I wish I didn't have to leave.

sad

My bed is so warm and cosy.

surprised

I can't believe that she is shouting at me.

Can you match the facial expression with its label and find the thought you think best fits that emotion?

disappointed

I shouldn't have thrown that stone even though I was cross.

ashamed

My painting will never look as good as hers.

jealous

I don't like to be on my own.

proud

My sister sang the best song in the concert.

lonely

I wish that I hadn't chosen this sandwich.

worried

Why are all the lights flickering?

Can you decide which emotion each of these characters is feeling? Draw the correct facial expression on their blank face.

Can you decide which emotion each of these characters is feeling? Draw the correct facial expression on their blank face.

How would you feel in each of these situations and can you explain why?

You are lost in the supermarket.

You get caught out in the rain.

You swam underwater for the first time.

Your best friend jumps out from behind a tree.

Today you are finishing school for the summer holidays.

Your goldfish is poorly.

Your friend is ill in hospital.

While you are playing a board game you realise your friend is cheating.

You were the last person to be chosen for the team in PE.

Your brother is deaf and people are making fun of him.

You don't like the sounds you hear at night.

Tomorrow is your birthday.

Your classmates choose you to represent them at the School Council.

Your mum allows your sister to watch TV after dinner, but not you.

Photocopy this sheet and create a set of voting cards for each child taking part in the discussion-based tasks.

Happy

Proud

Scared

Excited

Ashamed

Jealous

Disappointed

Worried

Lonely

Sad

Surprised

Angry

Place the pictures in order of emotional intensity.

Happy

Sad

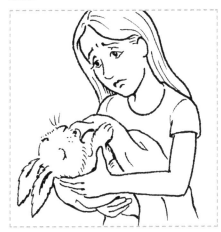 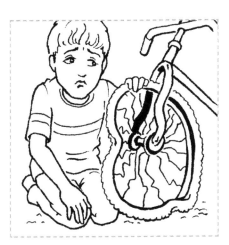 

Angry

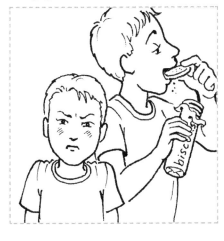  

Least intense ← → Most intense

Place the pictures in order of emotional intensity.

Scared

Surprised

Disappointed

Least intense		Most intense

Change each scenario below into one in which the character would feel happy. Draw the new scenes in the boxes provided.

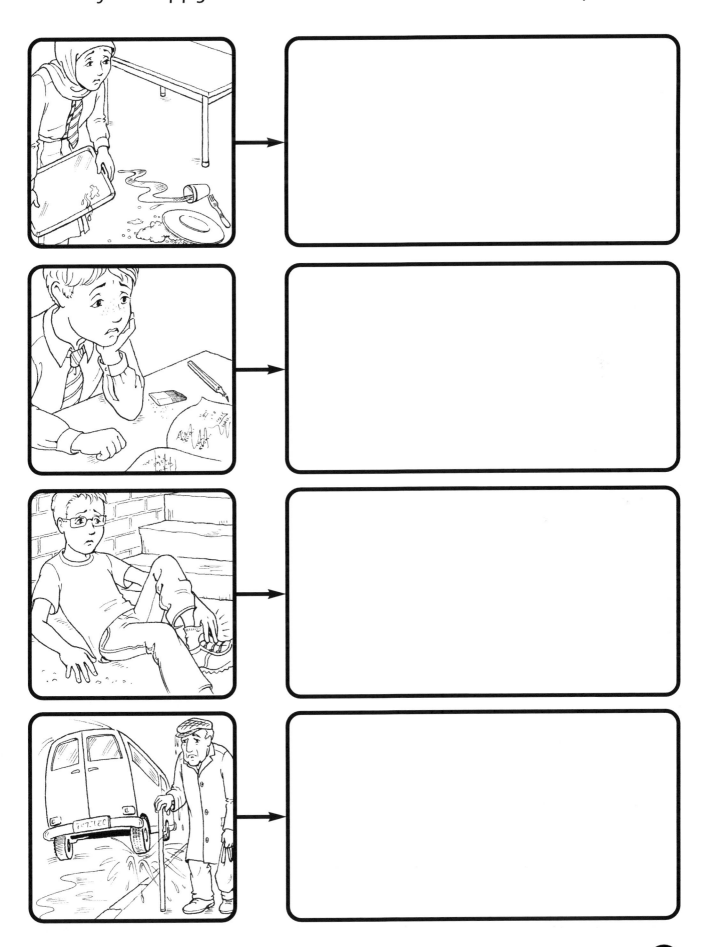

Which picture will change the emotion on the left to the new emotion on the right? Place a picture between each pair of emotions.

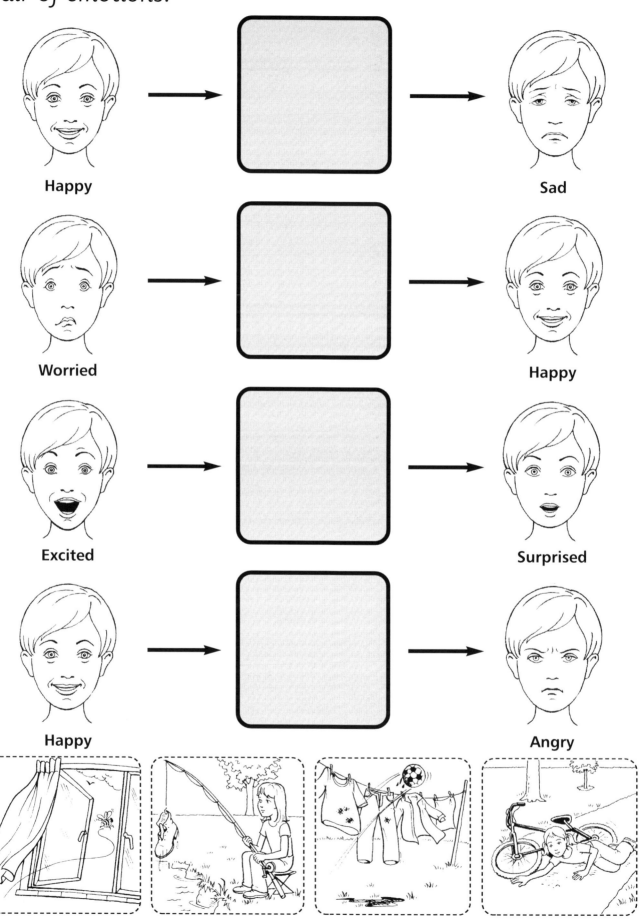

Happy

Sad

Worried

Happy

Excited

Surprised

Happy

Angry

Which picture will change the emotion on the left to the new emotion on the right? Place a picture between each pair of emotions.

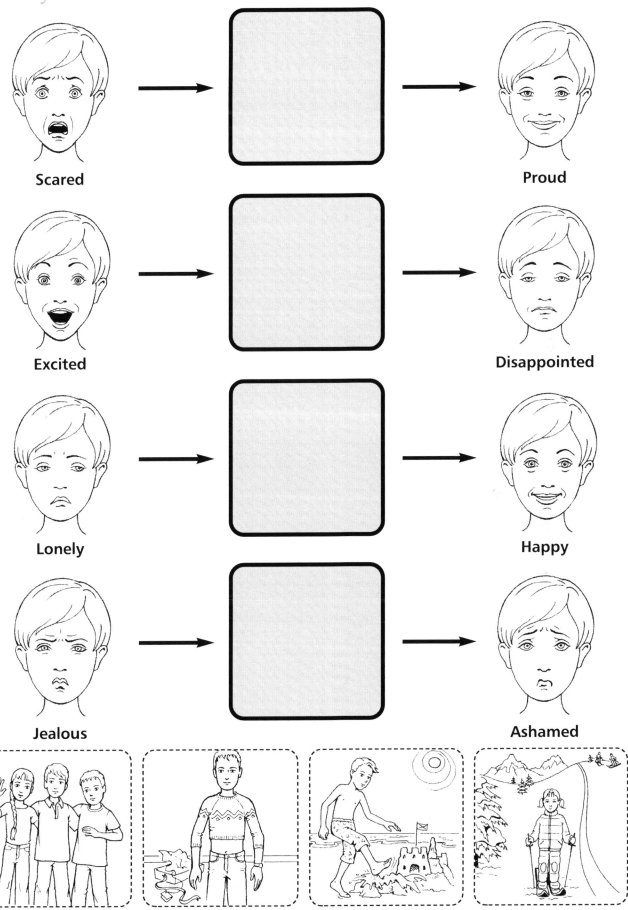

Scared → → **Proud**

Excited → → **Disappointed**

Lonely → → **Happy**

Jealous → → **Ashamed**

Draw a possible outcome for each scene below and then decide how the characters might feel.

Draw a possible outcome for each scene below and then decide how the characters might feel.

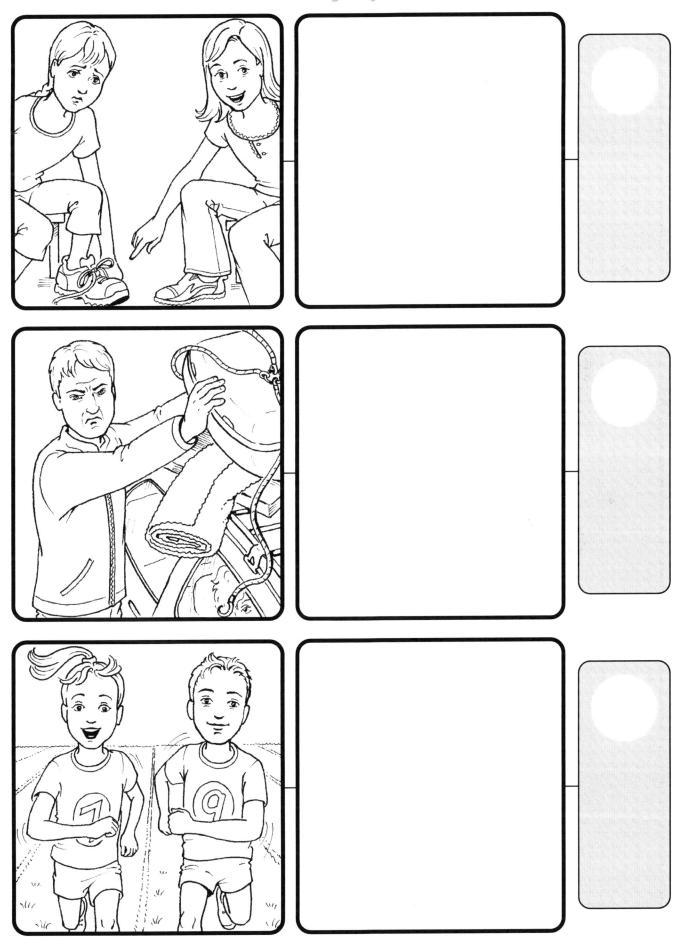

Discuss and choose an emotion for each scene and draw what happens next based on that emotion.

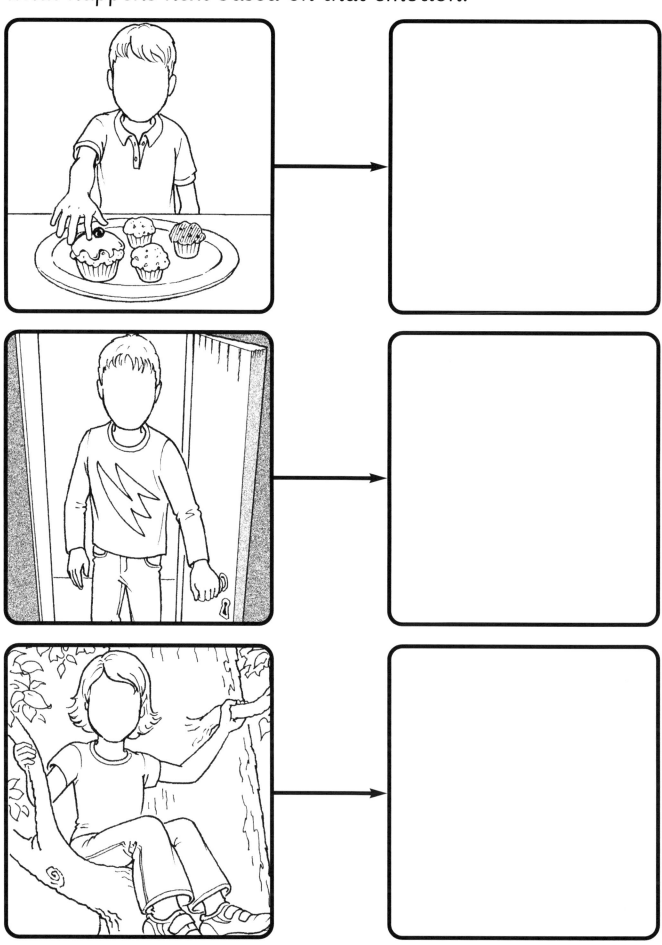

Permission to Photocopy

Discuss and choose an emotion for each scene and draw what happens next based on that emotion.

Look at the sequences below and fill in the blank faces to show how the emotions of the characters change.

© *Understanding Emotions* LDA

Permission to Photocopy

Look at the sequences below and fill in the blank faces to show how the emotions of the characters change.

Cut out these emotion faces to use with the activities.

Happy

Worried

Sad

Lonely

Angry

Proud

Scared

Ashamed

Excited

Disappointed

Surprised

Jealous